Following the Path: Highland Village Series

The MacCallum House
1798

Best wishes

Jim St Clair

7 August 1999

The UCCB Press acknowledges the support received for its publishing program from the Canada Council's Block Grants Program.

Cover design by Gail Jones
Book design by Gail Jones
Printed and bound in Canada by Kromar Printing Ltd., Winnipeg, Manitoba, Canada

Illustrations by Patsy MacAulay-MacKinnon. Photos courtesy of The Nova Scotia Highland Village Society. Period photographs from *A Taste of Scotland, Scottish Traditional Food* by Theodora FitzGibbon, specially prepared by George Morrison. J.M. Dent & Sons Ltd. London. © Theodora FitzGibbon, 1970

Canadian Cataloguing in Publication Data

St.Clair, James O.

The MacCallum house, 1798
(The Highland village series)
ISBN 0-920336-75-2
1. Tiree Island (Scotland) -- Social life and customs -- Juvenile literature. 2. Tiree Island (Scotland) -- Emigration and immigration -- Juvenile literature.
I. Title. II. Series.

DA880.H4S34 1999   j941.1'4   C99-950122-4

University College of Cape Breton Press
Box 5300, Sydney, Nova Scotia B1P 6L2
CANADA

MacCallum House

Introduction

The MacCallum House 1798 is the first of several books in the "Following The Path - The Highland Village Series," which will trace the lives of Mairi and Ruari MacCallum and their relatives from 1798 in rural Scotland to 1920 on Cape Breton Island.

The MacCallum House 1798 describes the life and times of Mairi and Ruari and their family living on the Island of Tiree. An unexpected letter from North America brings the possibility of great change in their lives. This book explores how they respond to an invitation to move away from their home.

The Nova Scotia Highland Village is a living history museum and cultural centre which celebrates, interprets and promotes the language and culture of Gaelic speaking Nova Scotians from the Highlands and Islands of Scotland. Located at Iona, in the central part of Cape Breton Island, the Village takes visitors on a journey through 180 years of life through period buildings and costumed staff carrying out traditional activities and chores. Among the buildings at the Highland Village is a replica of the house in which Ruari and Mairi lived. This book brings that to life.

We invite you to join us as we travel through time bringing history to life in the Highland Village Series.

Rodney Chaisson, Manager
Nova Scotia Highland Village Society

MacCallum House

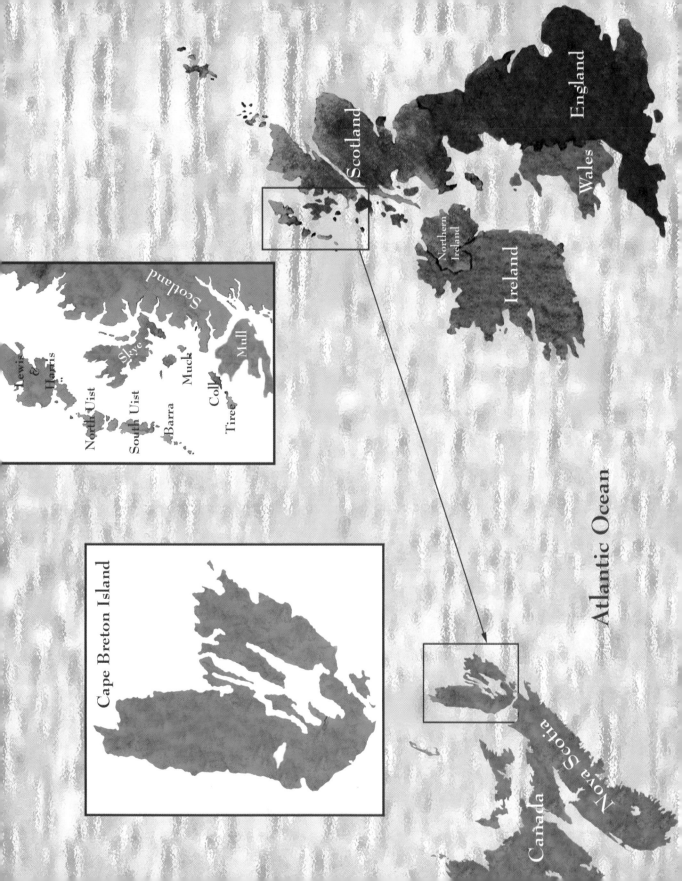

Mairi and Ruari
at Home in Tiree

Come, come along with me to meet two young people of long, long ago. Their names are Mairi and Ruari MacCallum. You may find their names quite unusual when compared to those we use today. Mairi is a Scottish Gaelic name similar to the English name Mary, while Ruari is similar to the name Rory, found in English. Gaelic is the language they use in their conversations and in their songs.

Indeed, everybody on the Island of Tiree, off the coast of Scotland, speaks Gaelic to each other. Even in church, the minister reads from a translation of the Bible in Gaelic. But Mairi and Ruari are learning some English from their Uncle Calum who is a sailor and has lived in North America. So they can say "how are you?" in English and know that it means the same as the Gaelic "Ciamur tha thu?" They often laugh at the sound of the English words which seem strange to them.

Mairi is just eight years old, while her brother is ten. Their small village of Kirkapol is on the coast of the Island of Tiree, spelled Tiriodh in the language of the people there. The island is small and

A thatched-roof, stone house like the one where Mairi and Ruari live.

quite flat with a number of little communities here and there along the shoreline.

As we come to Kirkapol, we see just seven houses, all built of stone with roofs made of dried grass called thatch. The buildings look very much

Ruari rests as his sister weeds the potato plants.

alike with their front doors facing the harbour. Potatoes and some other vegetables grow in small gardens behind the houses. Each family has a milk cow in the pasture at the foot of a small hill.

Tool to make holes in ploughed soil for planting potatoes.

Tool for hoeing or digging potatoes.

In front of the seven houses is a long stretch of beautiful beach with sand that is very white. Mairi and Ruari and the other children of Kirkapol play on the beach when the weather is fine. They run and skip and hop, often singing songs as they do. All of the young people are cousins. Their grandmother, another Mairi, lives in the middle house of the village with Uncle Calum. She often gives the children small pancakes as treats when they rest awhile in front of her house.

As there is no school in Kirkapol, the children spend their days playing or doing errands for their parents and their grandmother. Sometimes, Mairi and Ruari and their cousins climb to the top of the little hill behind their houses. Pink and blue and yellow wild flowers grow intermixed with clover and wild grasses.

The cattle and the sheep of the whole village stay up on the hill during the spring, the summer and the autumn. There is food and water for them up there. Ruari and Mairi go up almost daily to see if there are any new calves or lambs. Each animal is valuable to the family and must be cared for. Mairi loves the little lambs and often makes a pet of one.

If we were to go with them, from the top of the hill, we would see other islands across the dark blue sea, in the far distance. Some of these have very high mountains rising up into the sky. Mairi and Ruari often point them out and call them by name — Mull and Coll and Muck. They hope that some day they may go with their father in his small sailing boat to see the people on those islands with the high hills. They know that some of the residents there are uncles and aunts and cousins, but for now they just hear stories about them from older members of the family.

When they look down from the small hill, the young people can see their mothers working in the gardens. Sometimes their mothers are milking the cows or coming and going among the

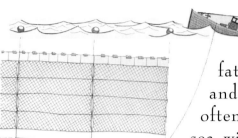

Nets trailing behind the fishing boats.

seven houses. Their fathers and uncles and older brothers often go out onto the sea with fishing nets trailing behind the fishing boats. From the hilltop, the vessels look tiny out on the huge bay and the houses appear quite dark as the sand surrounding them is glistening white.

Buoy made of sheepskin and tar, plugged with cork.

Many days in the early summer, when there is a good breeze and some sunshine, the people of the village go to the back side of the hill where there is a large swampy area. There, the men dig out squares of hard packed peat from the ground. It looks very much like dirt with moss and twigs mixed in. The women and children pile up the small blocks, one on top of another so that the wind and the sun can dry out the peat. When ignited in the fireplaces, these small packages of earth are the fuel for warmth and cooking.

Peat iron for
cutting peat.

In the autumn, when the blocks of
peat are dry, all of the women and
children except the
grandmother, go out
from the village
with baskets
woven with
twigs. They
place the peat in
the baskets and
tie the containers
to their backs and
shoulders. In this

Willow
basket for
carrying
peat.

way, they transport a supply of fuel to each house, with a large stack for grandmother.

Ruari is now old enough to carry a small basket strapped to his shoulders but Mairi is still too young. But she and the other younger children go with the rest to see how the work is done so they can help out when they are older. They also join in singing a work song which seems to make the difficult tasks go along more quickly.

**"o hee er rho;
o hee er rho"**

Although the words of the song are just nonsense sounds, they have a jolly ring to them. They seem to be "o hee er rho; o hee er rho." In this year of 1798, the people of Kirkapol work and sing together as their parents and grandparents have done for years. In this way, they provide food for their homes, fuel for the fire and some products to sell.

On days when the wind blows heavy rain across the island and angry-looking waves toss and turn in the bay, Mairi often learns from her mother how to clean the wool when it is cut

A pair of sheep shears is used to remove the fleece from the sheep.

from the sheep. Every twig and bit of dirt must be picked out and the wool formed into rolls. Now, she is just beginning to learn to twist the fibres of wool into yarn which the weavers will turn into blankets and material for

Sheep shears

clothing.

Ruari is learning from his father and uncles how to make ropes from strands of heather, a plant which grows in abundance on the far hillside. These ropes are needed for raising the sails of the boats. Both children are taking on tasks which will

Every twig and bit of dirt must be picked out of the wool.

benefit the family and the whole community.

Ruari and Mairi are growing up like the other children of the Island of Tiree without ever travelling very far. They go to church in the next village and sometimes visit relatives on the other side of the island. Life seems very peaceful and happy for these children in Kirkapol with its beautiful beach, its many colourful flowers and its small dark-looking stone houses with the thatched roofs. And so it is on Tiree, off the coast of Scotland, in 1798.

Hand tools used to remove dirt from the wool.

A Letter from Overseas

In the late afternoon on a day in June, Mairi and Ruari are sitting on a wooden bench placed against the front wall of their house. Mairi is playing with her kitten which she calls "piseag glas" which is translated into English as "grey kitten." The small cat is following a piece of string which Mairi is pulling on top of the sand. She laughs as the small animal tumbles and jumps in play.

With his pocket knife, Ruari is working at carving a wooden bowl out of a piece of driftwood which washed up on the shore. His father, Iain, has taught him the way to hold his knife and to cut with short strokes. If the bowl looks all right, he will give it to his grandmother who lives in the house next door.

From inside the house, they can hear their mother, Morag, singing as she works at spinning wool. The words of her song are known to both Mairi and Ruari and they begin to sing along - "o ho or, o ho ri, o ho or." The whirr of the weaving spindle blends with the tune.

Spinning wheel for spinning wool.

Their father and their uncle Calum sailed across the bay early on this morning. With them, they took many sacks of kernels of oats to be ground into oatmeal. Before a new wind-powered grinding mill was built, people had to grind oats for themselves with hand mills known as querns. But now the old grinding stones are replaced by the new facility at Scarinish across the bay.

Quern stone for grinding small amounts of oats.

Coming across the harbour, their father's boat is becoming larger and larger as it approaches the beach in front of the houses. They can see their uncle Calum starting to take down the sails as their father guides the boat with the tiller. The sun sparkles on the waves.

As they draw the boat up on the beach, the two men are talking with much excitement to each other and to the other men of the

Rideil - used for sifting grain.

village who come together to lift the sacks of oatmeal from the small boat. The bags of ground meal are placed inside the houses, two for each dwelling and three for grandmother's use. The families have oatmeal every day, sometimes for two meals.

Ciosan - storage basket for grain.

Mairi and Ruari can catch snatches of conversation among the adults as they go about their tasks of unloading the supplies from the boat. They hear the words "letter" and "Cape Breton" often spoken now as the women of the village come to the doorways of their houses to hear the news. There is much excitement in the various questions and answers.

Soon their mother calls Mairi and Ruari to come into the house for the evening meal. She has prepared porridge from the newly ground oatmeal and is making oatcakes as well. These small round cakes are a great favourite with everybody and are generally covered with butter and once in a great while with molasses.

Butter pats for shaping butter.

It is dark inside the house for there are only two windows in the front wall and one in the back wall. They are small openings covered with scraped skins from animals for glass is too expensive for the people of Kirkapol.

The fireplace for cooking food and providing heat is in the middle of the floor of the house. It is made of beach stones piled up. Within the circles of

stones are several blocks of peat, each burning slowly.

The smoke from the fire rises lazily up through the one-room cottage towards an opening in the thatch of the roof. There is no ceiling, just the underside of the woven dry grasses which keep out the rain and the wind. The smell of the peat is a bit sharp in the nostrils but it is just part of everyday life. The smoke continually darkens the timbers and the thatch overhead.

Ruari and Mairi sit around the peat fire on low stools. Their mother has been cooking the oatmeal porridge in a large iron pot hung by a long chain from one of the roof-rafters. The pot hangs just inches above the smouldering fire. On the side of the fireplace, very close to a piece of burning peat is a metal plate with holes in it. On it are oatcakes, now turning brown and almost ready to eat.

After their father gives thanks to God for their food, their mother takes the oatmeal out of the iron pot with a large wooden spoon. Ruari passes a pitcher of

Slabhraidh - potchain hung over the hearth.

Griddle- for baking oatcakes.

cream to each person while Mairi hands out the pewter spoons. In most houses, the spoons are made of wood, but Mairi's mother's mother gave her six pewter spoons at the time of her wedding. They are much treasured by the whole family.

Cast Iron cooking pot with a wooden spoon.

The bowls are carved from wood so each one is slightly different in shape and size. As there are no trees on the Island of Tiree, wood must be gathered along the shore where it washes up from shipwrecks. Every board and timber is put to use. Ruari and Mairi's uncle Calum has told them about all the big trees which he saw when he lived in North America. But the children find it very hard to understand what they look like and how they could grow so tall.

Wooden bowl with a handle, often used for putting porridge in.

After eating their porridge and enjoying several oatcakes which are just hot from the metal griddle, Ruari and Mairi do the tasks which they do every evening. Ruari carries in blocks of peat from the stack outside near the end wall of the cottage. He also brings two large wooden buckets full of fresh water from the spring not far from the village. Mairi washes out the bowls and cleans the pewter spoons and puts them away on the cupboard where supplies and dishes are kept.

A wooden drinking cup.

Their mother puts the remaining porridge and oatcakes away in heavy crocks stored in the base of the dresser. Their father has lit two cruisie lamps. These are metal bowls shaped like large tree leaves. They hold fish oil. From the oil extends a wick or piece of twisted fabric which is set on fire. The light is very little but, with the glow from the fire, it

Cruisie lamp - fish oil was often burned in these lamps; a wick lay in the spout of the top pan, while the lower pan caught the drips of oil for re-use.

MacCallum House

Cruisie lamp that uses four wicks.

provides some illumination inside the house.

Their father who is able to read Gaelic very well but has much difficulty in saying English words takes from his pocket a letter which he and Uncle Calum found waiting for them when they arrived at Scarinish in the morning. It was sent to them care of the minister, the Reverend Ewan Ross. It was five weeks on its journey from Cape Breton in North America.

For Mairi and Ruari, a letter is a very unusual object. People on Tiree rarely receive any mail for most of their business is done by word of mouth or recorded in large books called ledgers which are kept by merchants or by people who own the land on which the MacCallums live.

With his voice stumbling over the English words, their father begins to read the letter to Morag and Mairi and

Morag cleans wool while waiting for Iain to read the letter from Cape Breton in North America.

Ruari. After he finishes it, then he translates the contents into Gaelic for them. The letter is as follows:

Sydney
Cape Breton Island
North America

the tenth of May 1798 to:

Calum and Iain MacCallum
Kirkapol near Scarinish
Island of Tiree via Oban
North Britain (Scotland)

My dear friends in Tiree

I take great pleasure in sending a letter to you from far away Cape Breton Island in Nova Scotia in North America. I send greetings to you and to all your people from me and my wife. We speak of you often.

I write to tell you that I am able to apply for a large lot of land on this Island under new regulations from the Governor of this place. If cultivated and settled, the tracts of land could have deeds of ownership issued to the inhabitants within ten years.

When Calum was visiting us here, he saw the area with its fine forest, its brooks with fish and its rich flat lands. We talked at that time about what a fine place it would be if all of you would come here. You would at last be able to own your property just like nobility in North Britain. No more landlords. No more rents.

I am hoping to hear from you at your earliest convenience and that you will consider this new opportunity for the benefit of your children.

With greatest respects to your mother and other members of your family,

Your friend,
Alexander MacCallum

As the daylight fades, Mairi and Ruari's father explains to them that Alexander is a first cousin, the son of an uncle who once lived on the Island of Mull. He also points out that Alexander is working in Cape Breton after many years of being an officer in the army. He now has a store and a farm and is prospering.

Morag and Iain begin to talk about what it would mean to have their own land and be free of the rent which the landlord is now increasing every year. They tell the children not to worry about the letter for they will talk about it another evening. But Ruari and Mairi know that the letter is important. They even want to touch this piece of paper which has come from far away in North America and has so many words in English.

Before they go to bed in sleeping cupboards which are at the far side of the room, they look around their home, this one-room stone house with its peat fire providing warmth and light. Their heads are so full of thoughts that they

The sleeping cupboards are located at the far side of this one-room stone house.

don't even hear their father's words as he reads a section from the Bible before they say goodnight to each other.

The letter - an unexpected arrival - has brought new ideas to Mairi and Ruari. Would they sail overseas in their father's sailing boat? Would they actually see and touch a tree? Could they take their pet lambs and the little grey kitty? The light from the cruisie lamps creates many flickering shadows as the two young people lie down to rest in their box beds on the Island of Tiree.

Uncertainty

As Ruari begins to wake up the next morning, he remembers a few images from a dream he has just had. He seemed to be on a large ship which was sailing backwards. He had dropped his pocket knife over the side and he could see it going down and down in the water. That is all that he remembers but he knows that the dream has made him  feel unhappy. He hopes that he can tell it to his grandmother for she believes that dreams tell the future. He reaches out for his small knife to be sure it is safe.

This morning, a strong wind is blowing over the roof of the house. He can hear it whistling as it passes through the top layers of thatch. Perhaps, later on in the day he will have to go up on the roof with his father to replace some of the covering for often a strong wind causes the thatch to blow away. But, the wind and rain coming from the west will keep them from outdoor tasks, at least for a time.

When the wind dies down for a moment, he can hear the voices of his father and mother in conversation.

Morag rekindles the peat fire in early morning.

Only a thin panel of wood separates his box bed from the one room of the house. Already, the smoke from the rekindled peat fire is circulating through the house. Each evening his mother is always careful to "smoor" or cover over some embers of the dying fire so that there will be hot coals to ignite the blocks of peat for the new day. It is considered very unlucky to lose the fire for the embers would then have to be brought from another house as there are no matches.

As he leaves his narrow bed, he pulls on a second pair of knitted socks before he puts on moccasin-like shoes made from animal skins. His father greets him with a blessing for the day, while his mother pours fresh water into a basin so that he can wash his face. Although light is showing through the windows of the house, all agree that the day is dark and stormy. As the wind and rain hit the front door, they sit close to the warmth of the peat fire.

Mairi appears from her sleeping cupboard with her hair all tousled. She sits on her father's lap while her mother combs out her hair and fits a small cotton cap over her head, a covering very much like her own. Mairi then searches for her kitten which usually sleeps in some hay in the part of the house set aside for the animals in the winter. But the kitten is not to be found right now.

As the family sits on small round stools around the peat fire, Iain, their father, takes from the cupboard one of the few books stored there. From the Bible, he reads one of the psalms which praises God for the new day and all the goodness of the earth. After closing the Bible, he announces they will pray and thank God for their food.

Following the "amen," Morag ladles out oatmeal from the big kettle hanging by an iron hook over the fire. The cream is passed around from person to person. A little sprinkling of salt is also added to each person's portion of the breakfast.

Bowl in which milk was placed until the cream rose to the top.

Ruari and his father inspect the roof.

As they come to the end of their meal, they notice that the wind is shifting to the south and the heavy rain is turning to showers. Ruari and his father go outside to bring in the blocks of peat for the day. They then inspect the roof to see if any thatch is missing, but all is well. As he looks at the sky, Iain says that there will be sun before evening. He and Ruari then go to the small garden to pull out the weeds from around the potato plants. As the ground is soft after the rain, the weeds are easy to pick out.

Mairi and her mother go to the pasture to milk the cow every morning and night.

Mairi and her mother wash the bowls and spoons and put them away on the cupboard. Then, they go to the pasture to milk the cow as they do every morning and night. They carry the milk back to the house in small wooden buckets and put some aside to take to grandmother later on in the day.

A wooden bucket with a piece of skin tied round its mouth, used to carry milk.

Seating themselves by the fire, Morag and Mairi prepare to pick twigs and thistles out of the wool heaped in wicker baskets. After the wool is cleaned, then Morag will begin to twist it into skeins of yarn. But before she

Milk Bucket/ Cuinneag - a wooden bucket used to collect the milk from cows.

MacCallum House

Morag picks twigs and thistles out of the wool.

begins, Morag asks her husband to read the letter to them again.

Ruari tries to say the strange words which his father reads in English -"Cape

Breton" - "benefit" - "children" - but finds them very hard to pronounce. After his father puts the letter away in one of the chests where papers are kept, Ruari asks his father about the offer of land mentioned in the letter. "Would there be a landowner and a person collecting rent?" With a glance at their mother, their father says, "no, we would own our land, to do with as we wish. Never again could a landlord tell us what to do."

Dyeing pot - used to boil dye into the wool.

After helping his father mend fishing nets by sewing up holes with very hard thread made of tightly spun wool, Ruari goes along to his uncle's house. Mairi runs to catch up with him for she knows that Uncle Calum will spend a few hours with them and their

Needle for making and mending fishing nets.

MacCallum House

cousins in showing them how to read in Gaelic and in teaching them some words in English.

When they meet at grandmother's house, the cousins all speak with each other about the letter that came from overseas from their cousin, Alexander MacCallum, in far off Cape Breton. The oldest of the cousins, Peter, announces that he wants to go to see this new place, while Suisi, who is seven years old, says that she wants to stay right where she is and play on the sand and go for walks up into the hills.

Uncle Calum tells all of them before they begin their lessons, that tonight the whole village will meet here at Grandmother's house to talk about the letter and to ask God to guide them in any decisions that they may make.

Ruari thinks about the letter before tonight's gathering.

Then Uncle Calum begins by pronouncing each English word twice and asking them to say it with him the third time - "Cape Breton" - "North America"

- "sailing boat" - "children" - "property" - until they all start to laugh at the funny sounds of the words which they are saying.

And so with work and learning and conversation, the day goes past the mid point. The sky starts to brighten up and then some blue sky is seen far away over the sea where the distant islands are dark shapes on the horizon. The wind lessens and the rain is over. The young people return to their own houses for they know that their parents will want them to help with the animals and with the gardens and other work. But all know that tonight's gathering will be more than just an ordinary get-together or ceilidh. There had been a thoughtful look on Uncle Calum's face as he talked about what he had seen overseas. And so, this day in June 1798 is spent on an island off the coast of Scotland.

The Decision

On Tiree, in the spring and early summer, the evenings are very long for the twilight lasts until nearly midnight. The sounds of the sheep calling to young lambs can be heard in the distance. Mairi often thinks she can make out the baaing from the little lamb which she helped to raise when its mother died. It still comes to her when she walks among the sheep.

The milk cow in the little field behind their house calls to the other cattle grazing in the distance and responses can be heard. After her mother finishes milking, Mairi carries home the milk from "Mol" which is her name for the small

Fetter - a rope used to tie a cow's legs while it was being milked.

Mairi named the black cow "Mol."

black cow. The milk is divided between her grandmother's and her mother's wooden buckets.

The half dozen hens are slowly walking around the outside of the small stone structure where they roost at night. They are picking up small bits of grain and an occasional tiny pebble needed for their gullets. Their clucking is constant and shows they are content.

Along the shore line in front of the village, many sea birds are riding the waves while the shore birds walk through the seaweed hoping to find their evening meal. The gulls and the herons are very plentiful. Cormorants may be seen as they gather on the rocks at the far end of the beach. Their black feathers glisten in

the distance. Often, the people of the village gather eggs from the nests of these huge birds if the door-yard hens are not laying eggs.

After finishing her tasks, Mairi begins to tease her little grey kitten "Piseag." The small pet chases a piece of yarn attached to a wooden stick . After some minutes of play, Mairi pours a dipper of milk into a small wooden bowl near the stone wall of the house. Piseag and Mairi are very attached to one another.

When the evening chores are all completed, the young boys from the

various houses of Kirkapol begin to race along the white sand. They are calling to each other as one outdistances another in friendly competition to see who can run the fastest. Ruari and the other boys come to be dark spots at the far end of the beach. The white sand glistens in the slanting rays of the setting sun.

From each of the three houses on both sides of Grandmother's stone cottage, the adults gather on the shore in front of the old lady's home. The men are wearing thick woolen sweaters while the women have shawls of homespun cloth over their shoulders. White close-fitting caps cover their heads.

The women covered their heads with white close-fitting caps.

Some carry low stools from their houses while others position drift-wood logs around the doorway. Uncle Calum helps his mother to settle into a wooden chair with a back to it, just within her house so that she is warmed by the heat of the peat fire inside but can hear all that is said and add her opinion. The family has great respect for grandmother.

Most of the women have brought their baskets of wool with them. They can use this time to remove bits of dirt or small twigs entangled in the fibres. Some of the men have brought their small knives to work at carving out the wooden bowls during the discussion of the letter received from overseas.

Mairi and one of her cousins sit and talk in front of grandmother's house.

The young girls, Mairi and her six cousins, sit together. They talk among themselves as their uncles and aunts and their brothers settle in a circle around the doorway. In the warmth of a Tiree evening, everybody feels comfortable and at ease. For this small community is just one large extended family, all related and very familiar with each other.

Mairi and Ruari's father, Iain MacCallum has brought the large Gaelic Bible, bound with black leather, for he feels that they must hear the word of God before they begin to talk about the future. And so, he reads from the 46th psalm "God is our refuge and stronghold, a timely help in trouble. . ." When he finishes with the words "the Lord of Hosts is with us and the God of Jacob is our fortress," all join in saying "Amen."

The words of this psalm are very familiar to them all, even the children. Uncle Calum has been using this passage in his

instruction of the children. Old Mairi, the mother (or mother-in-law) and grandmother of all twenty-five people gathered, with a slight catch in her voice praises her son for his reading. "Indeed, indeed," she says, "your voice is so like your dear father's as you read the word of God." Her blue eyes are bright with tears as she says "I wish he were here to help us now."

But Grandfather had died before young Mairi was born; he drowned when coming from the mainland of Scotland in a small boat.

With the sound of the waves in the distance and the smell of the smoke from the peat fires surrounding them, the various members of the MacCallum family speak in turn. Each person tries to find the words to express their concerns and their fears about moving to Cape Breton. The children listen and some of the younger ones find comfortable laps and fall asleep, with the sound of familiar voices in their ears.

People talk about how the rents required by the landlord are increasing each year and how the market for selling their cattle is declining. Some say that they should talk to the representative of the landlord, the tacksman, Alexander Graham. But others say he is hard- minded and will not listen.

They share stories they have heard about the land of Cape Breton. Uncle Calum tells them about the cold and the snow of winter, almost unknown to them here on Tiree. But he also tells them of

the warm summers and the soil which grows beautiful potatoes. Uncle Ruari, the youngest of the adults and married for only four years, keeps mentioning the promise of their cousin in Cape Breton — that they can all own land if they go there.

Although children do not often add their opinions in such gatherings of the adults in family groups, Mairi who has been dozing in her father's lap, wakes up when Aunt Grace asks what they could take with them if they were to leave their stone cottages for a new home. Mairi with a sleepy voice announces to all, "I will not go to this Cape Breton if I have to leave Piseag here for nobody will give him a bowl of milk." Everybody smiles at Mairi's comment, but they know that she has said something they all feel. Can they really leave all that is familiar behind them?

In the gathering darkness, oatcakes and cups of milk and sweetened water are handed around the group by the mothers. The men are given small portions of whiskey mixed with water. After more conversation, people grow silent, each filled with thoughts. Then, old Mairi, the mother and grandmother, begins to speak in a quiet, steady voice:

Oatcakes

"When I was a child, many years ago, an old lady of our village could foretell the future by reading the leavings of tea. These leaves were saved from time to time for tea was very expensive then. One day, she read my future and told me that when I was very

Grandmother was told that some day she would travel in a great boat.

old I would travel in a great boat. That time which she could see has come and I am willing to leave here. I know that we must look to the future and trust in God's help." With that said, she rises slowly from her chair and goes inside her old stone cottage to sit by the peat fire glowing on the hearth. And then all go slowly to their own houses with looks of sadness and also of hope on their faces. They now know they will all leave Tiree to go to Cape Breton.

Iain carries the sleeping Mairi in his arms while Ruari walks with his mother as he carries her wool basket back to their home. He realizes that life will never be the same after this night. He helps his mother "smoor" or bank the embers of the fire so that there will be a spark or two remaining in the morning for the new day. Then all go to sleep and to dream in the quiet night of Tiree.

Then all to sleep and to dream in the quiet night of Tiree.

The Leaving

A year after receiving the letter, the MacCallums of Tiree, are ready to leave for Cape Breton. A large vessel with three masts is in the bay. Along with several other family groups from nearby communities, the MacCallums will travel to the unknown Island of Cape Breton in Nova Scotia. After months of preparation, all is in readiness for the journey.

As Ruari awakes in the early morning of this last day in the familiar surroundings, he hears the wind blowing through the thatch above his head. This spring, no repairs have been made to the roof since the house will be left empty when the family departs. In the dim light, he looks at the timbers holding the roof in place. They are blackened with years of peat smoke. But now no clothes

Rauri and his mother outside their home on this last day in Tiree.

or vegetables are hanging from the rafters as they once did for all is packed in chests and stored away on the vessel, a ship named "Constant."

Mairi stretches in her bed inside the familiar sleeping cupboard and opens her eyes. She knows that this day will be different than any she has ever experienced. The bed clothes must be folded and placed in the chest still to be taken from the house. All that is left of her possessions are the shawl which she will wear on board ship and a large woven basket.

In this basket is a small New Testament in Gaelic and English, a book which Uncle Calum gave her before he left Kirkapol last September to go to Cape Breton to arrange for the land where they would begin a new life. In a small crockery jar, Mairi has placed a handful of sand from the beach so she can always remember how Tiree looks. There will be a place in the basket for Piseag who is now a full-grown cat. After much pleading, she was able to persuade her father that she could try to take her pet with her. But he warned her that food would be in short supply on the boat and the cat might not survive the journey.

For the last time, Mairi and Ruari close the doors to their sleeping cupboards. Their mother has warm milk and oatmeal porridge ready as they sit on the low stools by the hearth. Only a very small fire is burning. No blocks of peat are stacked inside the door or along the outside wall of their house for the family has cut no fuel from the ground this year.

As they sit by the familiar peat fire, their father speaks a blessing on the food and prays for safety on the coming journey. Nobody has much to say; all are uneasy about leaving Kirkapol. But the time has come, the time which seemed so far away last summer as the family sat in the twilight of an evening in front of Grandmother's house.

And so it is that Mairi and Ruari MacCallum look around their childhood home. It seems strangely empty for all the clothes and blankets are packed away in chests. Their wooden dishes are no longer on the cupboard. Their mother's pewter spoons are stored away in the basket which she will carry on board the

The pewter spoons are stored away in this basket which Morag will carry on board the ship.

ship. Also, in it are her supply of herbs
and dried plants useful for illnesses.
The unspun wool is at the bottom of a
big barrel of household tools and goods.
Nothing is left except the bare stone
walls and the ring of stones which
creates the hearth.

thistle

　　　As their father and mother pack
the remaining blankets and clothes in
the last chest, Mairi and Ruari and
some of their cousins from the other
houses walk up into the hills behind
the village. The wild flowers are in
bloom everywhere. Except for the
wind and the sound of the seagulls,
it is strangely quiet. For the sheep and
the cattle which once grazed here are

The large vessel, Constant, on which they will travel waits in the harbour.

gone, sold to neighbors or buyers in other villages. In the harbour, they can see the large vessel on which they will travel for five or six weeks. It is moving up and down as waves come in from the open sea. In the far distance, they see the neighboring islands, places they will not visit now. And there at the foot of the hill, with just wisps of smoke coming through the thatch, are the seven houses, dark patches on the white sand of the shore. This view will remain in Mairi's memory throughout her life. In her old age, she will tell her great-grandchildren of her recollection of her childhood in Kirkapol.

It is strange to look out from the hillside and not see any of the small fishing boats which their fathers and older brothers used in the days gone by. It is even more strange for them to realize that they may never again come to this spot. To mark the occasion, they all pile up small stones to make a monument at the edge of the hill. This cairn will remain for years.

As they come down from their last trip across the pasture and the garden where potatoes and other vegetables once grew, they can hear their parents singing a song of Tiree as they stand on the shore by the small boats which will transport them to the larger vessel. Then led by Iain, they join in prayer. With the voice of old Mairi rising clear and strong, they sing a metrical version of the 121st Psalm - "Unto the hills around..."

After Uncle Ruari helps grandmother into the boat, she stands for a moment with her warm shawl wrapped around her. Then she takes off her white cap and lets her grey hair blow in the breeze. "I came here as a bride fifty years ago and never expected to leave. But I want a good future for you all, and so I go, trusting in God. I leave your father's body here but take in my pocket some soil from his grave to be placed in my final resting place, wherever that will be. Don't forget, my dears." She turns her back on Kirkapol as she looks to the open sea as she replaces her cap.

Grandmother takes her cap off and lets the wind blow through her hair.

At the last minute, Mairi cannot find her cat. She looks everywhere and begins to cry. But then Piseag comes out of the stone cottage with a look of surprise. She found no food in the usual place. As Mairi gathers her in her arms and puts her in the basket, the grown-up kitten purrs with content to be warm and cherished, unaware of the coming adventure.

As the anchor is raised and the sails are unfurled and the long journey to

Cape Breton begins. Mairi and Ruari stand with their father and mother, their grandmother, their cousins and aunts and uncles at the rail of the vessel. Slowly and then more rapidly, the sailing ship moves towards the open sea and the future. The seven stone houses of Kirkapol grow smaller and smaller until they are just dots on the white sand of the shore.

No more will these young people smell the peat fire on the hearth or go among the houses lined up the shore. But etched in their memories will be the vision of the "dark" houses of their childhood, and the way of life of Kirkapol. New opportunities await them in a new land. They carry with them what they can of the old world, sand from the shore, their songs, a cat, their grandmother, memories of a family and a trust in God.

Unfamiliar Terms

cairn - a mound or heap of stones set up as a marker.

ceilidh - a gathering or party with music and stories and food.

Ciamur tha thu? - translated into English as "How are you?"

ciosan - a storage basket for grain.

Coll - an island near Tiree.

cormorants - large web-footed water birds having hooked bills and a pouch under their beaks.

crock - a jar or pot made of clay.

cruisie lamps - metal bowls shaped like leaves to hold fish oil. From the oil extends a wick which is set on fire to provide light.

cuinneag - a wooden milk bucket.

Gaelic - a language and culture found in parts of Europe and North America.

griddle - a pan used for cooking oatcakes.

heather - a hardy evergreen shrub with pink flowers.

heron - any of several wading birds, having a long neck, a long, slender bill, and long legs.

Kirkapol - a small village on the coast of the island of Tiree.

landlord - a person who owns and rents out real estate.

leavings of tea - tea leaves now found inside a tea bag.

ledger - a book used for keeping records in the days before cash registers and computers.

Mairi - a name similar to the English name Mary.

metrical version - written as poetry.

Mol - Mairi's name for the small black cow from which they get their milk.

Muck - an island near Tiree.

Mull - an island near Tiree.

pewter - a kind of metal, made from tin and lead, used to make dishes, forks, knives and spoons.

piseag glas - translated into English as grey kitten.

psalms - a book in the Bible with many poems which were often sung in churches and in homes.

quern - a hand mill used to grind oats.

rideil - a pan with holes in the bottom used for sifting grain.

Ruari - a name often translated into English as Roderick and sometimes Rory for short.

Scarinish - a village across the bay from Kirkapol.

slabhraidh - a pot chain which hung over the hearth.

sleeping cupboards - places for sleeping which had doors to shut out drafts; also known as box beds.

tacksman - the person who collects rents from small farmers who don't own their own land and then gives most of that money to the person who owns the land.

thatch - a covering of reeds, straw, etc. arranged on a roof so as to shed water.

thistles - one of various prickly plants; especially the bull thistle, the national emblem of Scotland.

Tiriodh - The island whose name is translated in English as Tiree.

tousled - untidy